FOREWORD by **KEGBUSTER**

If there was a long service medal for the total dedication to the real ale movement I cannot think of anyone more entitled to it than me. I have seen it all! From the days when the media treated a CAMRA demo with the same amused condescension they adopted when covering a folk dance round a maypole; big bellied bierdos up to their silly games again, right up to today when nearly 35,000 members attend the CAMRA AGM with another 50,000 locked outside.

Where have all the years gone? What happened to the Breathalyser effect, the Hofmeister Bear and "I'm only here for the beer!"? Sometimes, when I'm having a pee, I look through the window of my traditional local, *The Duck 'n' Weave*, corner of Great Noseblast Street, members only, and I watch the heaving mob glued to the counter laughing and drinking, happily oblivious that all of this would have been swept away had it not been for me and CAMRA!

Good beer was *that* close to extinction 20 odd years ago in the hey day of the massive, steam rolling conglomerates who used the same word, 'outlet' to describe their pubs and sewage pipes, but, cometh the hour, cometh the man! I offered my massive knowledge of beer drinking and pub lore, free and gratis to the disheartened, beaten rabble which was CAMRA and in no time turned them into an aggressive militant force ready to take on Grotnys and Twitbreads, the monopolies and murders commission and any other threat to a quiet pint.

It was I who exposed the Grotnys 'Hard Men' for what they were; pretty actors in TV beer commercials who dashed into a swan sur-rounded riverside pub weari
and then, eyelids fluttering,

Surly landlords and miserab
mark I saved! They'd been t
they were a species to be protected and treated with respect! Sadly, even today there are still people who don't fully appreciate having an excellent pint of Crudgington 6X shoved roughly towards them or paddling in the pools of beer on the bar top for their change! Believe me, O Ye of Little Faith, if it were not for my sweat and determination there would be *no* Crudgie and the face across the counter, exuding plastic bonhomie would belong to a graduate of a 3 day 'running a pub' course at Twitbreads 'No Cellars' charm school!

It all seems so long ago when I used to turn purple trying to convince young Jackson to spell 'Peculier' without an 'A' and is it really more than two decades since Linda Lusardi helped me demonstrate that the jelly from a hot meat pie, if it's any good at all, has to slide down much further than your armpit? Small things, yet all part of the great campaign which regretfully has to be fought even harder today as the enemy becomes bigger and more insensitive to non eco-

nomic factors like enjoyment, taste and choice. The big brewers are even more determined to turn all of our pubs into Louis Quinze steak bars, with a bigger mark up on food and wine than beer and drive you back into your own home! Here you can sit with the Hoover roaring or the thump-thump of your shirt being ironed and drink supermarket 'Moby Dick', real draught in a tin while watching Sky TV coverage of the Dogshitting Championships from Hove. Fantastic!

We must go on fighting if there is to be any hope of preserving the inalienable right of getting up at least 6 times during the night for a pee, waking with a 'Riverdance' head and knowing that the throbbing is down to good traditional beer from a good traditional pub and not some chemical witch pee from alleged brewers owned by Mitsubishi or I.G. Farben!

A word of warning! Have I over used 'traditional' a little too much? If this is true, I'm sorry but don't for one moment think that these are the ramblings of some silly old fart meandering down memory lane in search of Hovis and a women under a bridge for tuppence ha'penny! Far from it. Maybe I never had a bicycle as a kid but I am as vital today as I was on my first D and D appearance (a trumped up charge) and am quite happy to 'go outside' with any man or woman at any time. Understood? Good!

Keep an eye out for me in your local boozer. I'm round most of the UK's pubs and beer festivals and welcome a brief chat about beer and pub grub, but one thing! Please don't ask me to settle arguments about sport or get involved in quizzes! There's nothing worse than going out for a bevvy and some prat spoils your evening by

asking you to fill in the missing spaces in the following "— is the answer to the universe and everything!" That really brasses me off!

Your Champion,

KEGBUSTER

COMING UP TO MY 70,000TH PINT OF CRUDGINGTONS 6X

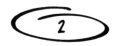

Author: Bill Tidy

Published by CAMRA Books,
Campaign for Real Ale, 230 Hatfield Road, St Albans AL1 4LW
Tel: (01727) 867201 Fax: (01727) 867670

Managing Editor: Mark Webb
Editor: Anne Bartasiene
Layout: McKie Associates

ISBN 1-85249-134-5

First Edition, August 1997

OFFICIAL: "ALE" PIZZA IS KEG

CAMRA doesn't just protect your pint but your pizza, too!
Trading Standards officials are investigating a "real ale" pizza.
Feb. '94

AMBULANCE TO THE RESCUE

REAL ale enthusiasts at The Rose & Crown at Orrell near Wigan need never feel tempted to drink and drive again now hosts Terry and Karen McPhelim have invested in a drinkers' ambulance to get them home safely - and legally!
March '95

Swoop by trading standards officers shows massive under measure fraud on drinkers

£5m SHORT PINT SCAM

CAMRA'S war against short pints has flared into new life following a dramatic swoop on chiselling landlords by Shropshire trading standards officers. They found just two pubs out of 25 serving a 20-ounce pint.
Jan. '97

NOT JUST A MESS BUT A NIGHTMARE

It may seem odd for What's Brewing to make common cause with Whitbread, but we are in complete agreement with the brewing giant on the scandal of importing cheap beer from Europe.
In the beginning thousands of Britons legitimately took advantage of the Open Market to visit Calais and other Channel ports to snap up beer and wine at a third of the price of this country. Then small-time "entrepreneurs" moved in, setting up discount warehouses in France and shipping large amounts of booze across the Channel.
May '94

It's frozen, concentrated and diluted - then you drink it

IT'S OFFICIAL: ALLIED WATER THEIR BEER

Allied Breweries have unveiled a revolutionary new beer dispense system which uses concentrated beer mixed with water at the point of sale.
Allied claim that the system is suitable for any style of beer, although it would obviously involve brewery conditioned keg brands.
Oct. '89

Beer giant's legal threat over brand name

S&N bully boys clobber a micro

A new Burnley brewery might be forced out of business by the bullying tactics of Scottish & Newcastle. S&N claim the name, Original Lion's Brews, is too close to Lion Brewery.
Nov.'91

Manchester landmark pub demolished during the night

GREENALLS=VANDALS

GIANT pub operator Greenalls faces prosecution following the overnight demolition of one of Manchester's most famous pubs. Tommy Ducks, famous for its past theatrical associations and a collection of underwear, was flattened before planning application had been considered by the city council.
April '93

Watchdogs back Campaign - may take legal action

CANNED ALES ARE A FRAUD

Trading standards officers dealt a body blow to fake "draught beers in cans" last month when they said the term was inappropriate for packaged beers.
March '93

US giant moves to grab Budvar

ROGER PROTZ REPORTS FROM THE CZECH REPUBLIC

The future of one of the world's classic breweries is once more in doubt. Both the western press and opinion in the Czech Republic suggests the independence of the Budweiser Budvar brewery is at risk.
March '94

At long last, the Scots join up for the ale revival

HARD GOING IN EDINBURGH - FOR KEG DRINKERS

Would you believe it? After years in the doldrums, cask beer is out of the closet and up on to the bar top in Scotland.
And all the ungrateful sods do is moan about it!
June '93

HANDOUTS FOR WINE, TWO FINGERS TO BEER

The European Beer Consumers Union, of which the Campaign is a founder member, has revealed the glaring discrepancy between the treatment of wine and beer within the European Community.

Wine is classified by the European Commission as an agricultural product, whereas beer is an industrial one. ... As a spokesman for the European Commission told us, "the wine growers get money to grow wine and they get money to dump it when they can't sell it."

Brewers enjoy no such treatment. If they cannot sell their beer, they pour it down the drain.
April '94

VICTORY DAY FOR CELEBRATION ALES

BREWERS big and small are in a ferment of excitement over the commercial possibilities of the VE Day celebrations on 8 May.

Special ales are being launched, pub events are being planned, and the Brewers Association has even brought out a booklet - Brewing for Victory.

April '95

YOU CAN FEEL IT IN YOUR BONES

DRINKING strengthens your bones, according to a recent study in California.

July '93

BREWING GIANT IN COURT FINE FOR FROZEN FOOD CON

A PLATE of frozen lasagne has cost brewing giant Whitbread and one of its pub managers £1,750 in fines and costs. The White Horse pub in Otterbourne, Hampshire, claimed on its menu it was selling "home-cooked" food. … The lasagne had been made in a factory where 2,880 meals are produced every hour!

Nov. '93

WOMEN WOOED BY PUBS

The pub trade's long fight to attract more women drinkers is paying off, according to a Public Attitudes Survey.

But increasing pubgoing by women is offsetting more drinking at home by men rather than creating a new market.

Only 20% of men go to the pub three times a week or more these days, compared to 30% five years ago, the survey of 20 000 respondents found.

May '94

MY PINT OF VIEW

How do you feel about your local landlord or landlady? When visiting your local do you suddenly feel 16 again? And what spurs you to get your round in?

Daft as these questions might seem, they form the basis of a recent study, which "challenges many popular myths about pubs - and about women."

Sept. '94

DOUBLE WHAMMY HITS PUBS

SALES of real ale are hit by a double whammy of alcopops and nitro-kegs, compounded by a growing trend towards drinking at home, according to research by Datamonitor.

Dec.'96

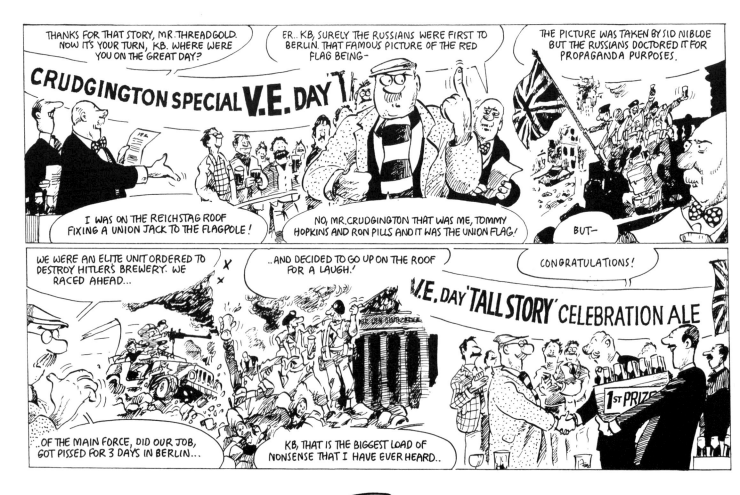

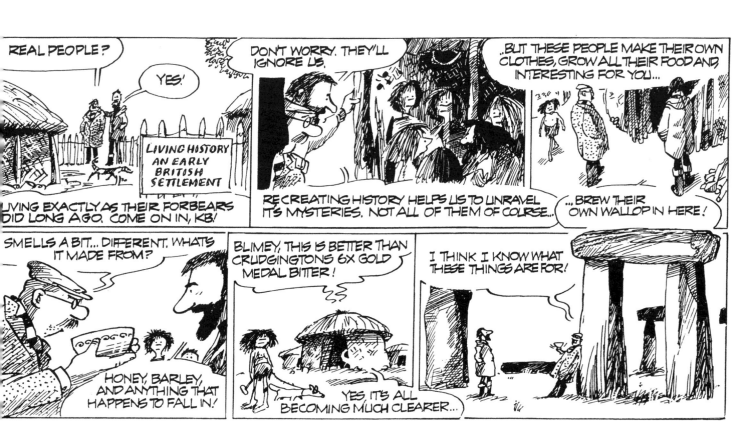

CUTTING COMMENTS

Reading through the GBBF press cuttings one usually learns little about beer - but an awful lot about journalists.

Fleet Street watchers will be familiar with the sloppy journalist's trick of relying on stereotypes: beards and bellies.
Sept. '95

Shock rise in country pub decline
DIVERSITY IS THE KEY TO SURVIVAL

Mansfield brewery's Neighbourhood Retailing scheme aims to increase landlords' income by helping them to become postmasters, newsagents and shopkeepers as well as publicans.
Aug. '95

PUBS AT RISK WARNS GOOD BEER GUIDE EVANS

"Pub character threatened by the tart-up teams and the chain pub restaurants"
Nov. '90

BEER GIANTS' DIRTY TRICKS

Britain's giant brewers have all produced lists of preferred guest beers that they are attempting to foist on their publicans.
JUNE '90

GENIAL HOST IS KEY TO GOOD PUB

GOOD publicans are one of the most important aspects of pubs according to a new report. Other issues raised included whether no-smoking areas or children's rooms were available and if there was plenty of seating or live music.
May '92

BAD TASTE IN DESIGNER PUBS

The reality is that combining all the best aspects of existing pubs into the design of another rarely produces a place where one can sit, feel comfortable and enjoy a drink.
June '89

HANG ON. I'M LISTING PUBS IN EUROPE SUITABLE FOR TWINNING WIV.

IT PROMOTES UNDERSTANDIN', ALL THAT BALLS. HMM, I FANCY...

..ITALY OR SPAIN. STRIKE UP A FRIENDSHIP AND ITS FREE DRINKS FOREVER ON YOUR HOLIDAYS!

ER..THIS IS A DEPRESSED INNER CITY AREA. WON'T IT BE DIFFICULT TO FIND...

..A TWIN IN THE SUN? THEY MIGHT TAKE ONE LOOK AND SAY—

THINK I'M STUPID?

I'LL SEND A PHOTO OF A TYPICAL...

NICE ENGLISH COUNTRY PUB!

RIGHT, THAT'S DONE. WHAT D'YOU WANT?

A PINT OF CRUDGIE AND A DEPRESSED, INNER CITY—

—I MEAN A PLOUGHMANS LUNCH!

DISABLED WOULD LIKE A DECENT PINT TOO

Guest beer writer Alan Stewart,

Feb. '95

PRICES DRIVING AWAY PUB TRADE

PRICE rises are keeping customers away from pubs. Drinkers are resorting to off-licences and clubs instead.

Oct. '91

LEASES ARE THREAT TO PUB HERITAGE

The headlong rush by national brewers to switch tenants to long leases is creating misery and hardship.

Oct. '91

Manchester's biggest independent brewer sells-out

BULLY BOYS BUY BODDIES

THE OFFICE of Fair Trading has given the go ahead to let Whitbread buy the Boddingtons and Higsons breweries

Nov, Dec. '89

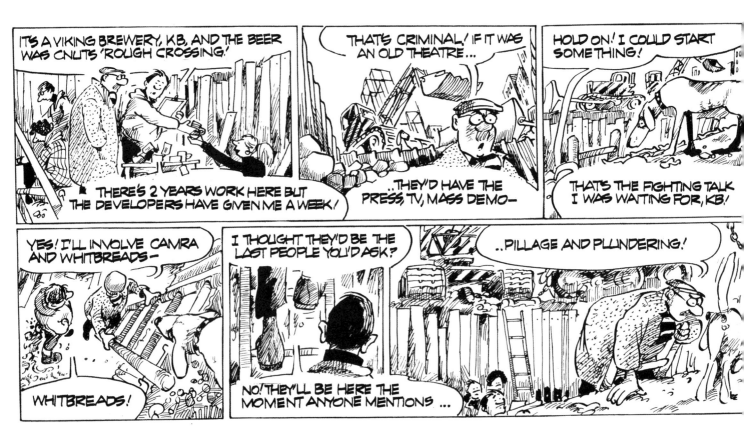

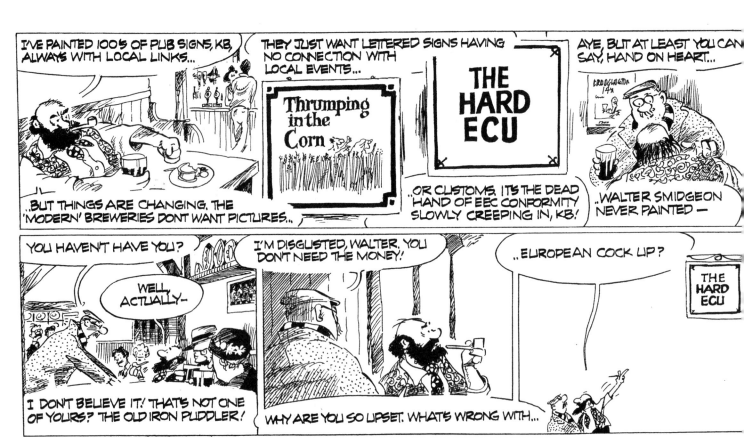